Piano Exam Pieces

ABRSM Grade 5

Selected from the 2021 & 2022 syllabus

Name

Date of exam

C000133256

Contents

page

Editor for ABRSM: Richard Jones

Other pieces for Grade 5

Published in 2020 by ABRSM (Publishing) Ltd, a wholly owned subsidiary of ABRSM, 4 London Wall Place, London EC2Y 5AU, United Kingdom

© 2020 by The Associated Board of the Royal Schools of Music Distributed worldwide by Oxford University Press

Music origination by Julia Bovee
Cover by Kate Benjamin & Andy Potts, with thanks to Brighton College
Printed in England by Caligraving Ltd, Thetford, Norfolk, on materials from sustainable sources.
P14653

La chevaleresque

No. 25 from *25 études faciles et progressives*, Op. 100

J. F. F. Burgmüller
(1806–74)

Johann Friedrich Franz Burgmüller, German by birth, settled in Paris after 1832. There he became a popular pianist and composer, improvising hundreds of salon pieces and composing much piano music for teaching purposes. Many of his short piano pieces, such as the *25 études faciles et progressives* (25 Easy and Progressive Studies), published in 1852, have fanciful or programmatic titles.

This piece is the last one in that collection. The 'knight errant' of the title is a medieval knight who rides in search of chivalrous (courteous and gallant) adventures. Section B (bars 17–24) of this ternary (ABA) piece acts like the trio in a minuet, contrasting in both movement and key (subdominant F). The reprise of A that follows is shortened to make way for a lengthy coda (bar 33 to the end).

Source: *25 études faciles et progressives*, Op. 100 (London: Schott, 1854). The dynamics and staccatos have been supplemented by the editor in accordance with those of the source.

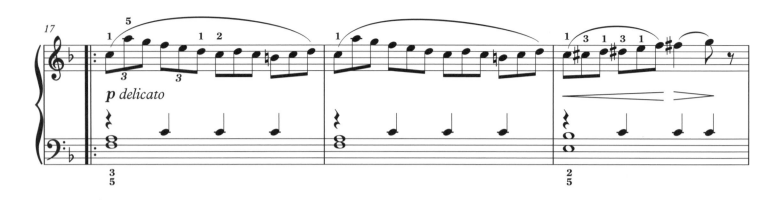

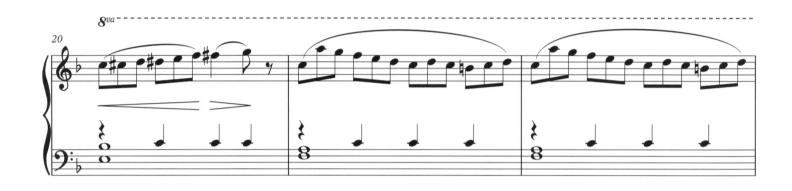

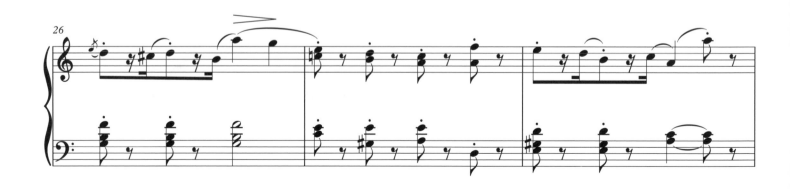

A:2

Presto

Second movement from Sonata No. 6

T. A. Arne
(1710–78)

Thomas Augustine Arne was a leading English composer for the theatre in the mid-18th century. He composed more than 90 stage works, chiefly for the Drury Lane and Covent Garden theatres. In a period that valued lyrical beauty above all, his success was due mainly to what a contemporary described as a 'God-given genius for melody'. Among his best-known songs is the patriotic 'Rule, Britannia'.

The Eight Sonatas of 1756, influenced by Domenico Scarlatti, were Arne's only published keyboard works. This Presto is written in the style of a jig, the English form of the French gigue. It is designed in rounded binary form (ABa) – similar to the later sonata form. The exposition (A, bars 1–25) contains two themes: the first in the tonic key, and the second (from bar 9) in the dominant. After the double-bar (bar 26), there is a 'development' (B) of the first theme, which modulates to several minor keys before closing in the tonic at bar 45. This is followed by a recapitulation of the second theme (a, from bar 46), now transposed to the tonic G.

Source: *VIII Sonatas or Lessons for the Harpsichord* (London: J. Walsh, 1756). The following notes are missing in the source and have been added by the editor: bar 33, right hand, *d″* sharp; bar 37, left hand, *d′*; bar 61, left hand, *G*. All dynamics are editorial suggestions only.

© 2020 by The Associated Board of the Royal Schools of Music

A:3

Toccata in G minor

HWV 586

G. F. Handel
(1685–1759)

[♩ = *c*.60]

The German-born composer George Frideric Handel was naturalised as an Englishman in 1727, having lived and worked mainly in London since 1710. He was not only a prolific composer but also a virtuoso keyboard player, as is clear from his famous keyboard competition with Domenico Scarlatti, in which honours were equally divided between the two contestants. It is not surprising, then, that keyboard music played an important part in Handel's output as a composer.

A toccata is a piece designed to demonstrate a player's touch, not only in fast passages but in ornamental writing, both of which are found in this Toccata in G minor. The piece probably dates from some time during Handel's first decade in London (1710–20). It is likely that he used short, unpublished keyboard pieces of this kind for teaching purposes.

Source: MS copy, London, British Library, R.M. 18.b.8. All slurs and dynamics are editorial suggestions only.

Adapted from Handel: *Selected Keyboard Works*, Book II, edited by Richard Jones (ABRSM)

B:1

Arctic Night

No. 1 from *Eskimos*, Op. 64

A. M. Beach
(1867–1944)

American-born Amy Marcy Beach was a child prodigy who studied piano at first with her mother, but was largely self-taught in composition. She became a virtuoso pianist and a prolific composer, writing more than 70 piano compositions and about 130 songs as well as chamber, choral and orchestral works.

Eskimos contains four pieces, all based on folk songs: 1. Arctic Night; 2. The Returning Hunter; 3. Exiles; 4. With Dog-Teams.

Source: first edition, *Eskimos: Characteristic Pieces for the Pianoforte*, Op. 64 (Boston: Arthur P. Schmidt, 1907). The following marks have been added by the editor: '*con Ped.*' (bar 1); *pp* in bar 23 (cf. bar 47); tie across bar-line to lowest right-hand notes in bars 23–4 (cf. bars 47–8); tie to lower right-hand notes in bars 39–40 (cf. bars 15–16).

B:2

Starry Dome

No. 15 from *Piano Meditation*

George Nevada
(1939–2014)

George Nevada, who was of German origin, composed a number of collections of pieces for solo piano, including *Romantic Impressions* (20 pieces), *Romantic Miniatures* (10 easy pieces), and *Piano Meditation*, subtitled 'Music for the New Age', from which 'Starry Dome' has been chosen. It paints a musical picture of the vast rounded dome of the sky at night and (from bar 25) of the twinkling of the stars.

Sweet Dreams

Douce rêverie

No. 21 from *Album pour enfants*, Op. 39

P. I. Tchaikovsky
(1840–93)

B:3

Pyotr Il'yich Tchaikovsky's *Album pour enfants* (Album for the Young) was written in 1878 after he had composed his Fourth Symphony and the opera *Eugene Onegin*. The set was subtitled '24 Easy Pieces (à la Schumann)' – a sign that the composer was thinking of Schumann's *Kinderscenen* (Scenes from Childhood) and *Album für die Jugend* (Album for the Young).

Source: *Oeuvres complètes pour le piano, Vol. IV: nouvelle édition revue et corrigé par l'aûteur* (Moscow: Jürgenson, 1893). 'con Ped.' (bar 1) is editorial, as is the accent in bar 24 (cf. bar 32). 'cresc.' has been added in bar 43; the source has only a hairpin *cresc.* in bar 44, but cf. bars 11–12.

© 1983 by The Associated Board of the Royal Schools of Music
Adapted from Tchaikovsky: *Album for the Young*, Op. 39, edited by Howard Ferguson (ABRSM)

Mister Trumpet Man

from *New Orleans Jazz Styles*

William Gillock
(1917–93)

William Gillock was an American music educator and composer of piano music. He lived and worked for many years in New Orleans, then later in the Dallas area. In his piano album *New Orleans Jazz Styles* Gillock states that jazz may have started in the honky-tonk amusement area of New Orleans around Basin Street. In 'Mister Trumpet Man' he gives a vivid impression of a jazz trumpeter displaying his skill to the accompaniment of big chords from the band.

C:2

Changing Times

from *Cool Piano 5*

Heather Hammond
(born 1963)

The British composer Heather Hammond studied piano and clarinet at the Leeds College of Music. She now runs a busy piano teaching practice in York. She also focuses on composing educational music and her six books of the *Cool Piano* series were published in 2003. The title of this piece has two meanings: it talks of changes that happen in modern life, but also of changes in the *time* of the piece, as shown by the different time signatures. Although the composer's metronome mark for the 'Quicker jazz waltz' section is ♩ = 168, students may prefer a slower tempo, for example ♩ = c.138.

C:3

Tarantella

No. 4 from *Musiques d'enfants*, Op. 65

Sergey Prokofiev
(1891–1953)

The Russian composer Sergey Prokofiev showed precocious talent at the piano and in composition at an early age. First taught by his mother, he was writing his earliest piano pieces by the age of five. Music written for children was highly regarded in the Soviet Union, and around the time of his return to Moscow in 1936 after 14 years abroad, he wrote three children's compositions in close succession: *Musiques d'enfants*, *Peter and the Wolf*, and Three Songs for Children.

Musiques d'enfants (Music for Children), which includes 'Tarantella', was written in 1935 and contains 12 pieces with fanciful or programmatic titles. The tarantella is a folk dance in quick 6/8 time from southern Italy, named after the town of Taranto. Prokofiev composes this tarantella in ternary form (ABA[1]), and the contrast between the minor mode of the outer A sections and the tonic major of the central B section (bars 33–48) is also typical of this dance.